Mystery Mob
and the April
Fools' Day Joker

Roger Hurn

Illustrated by
Stik

D0494745

RISING★STARS

X2000000127876

Rising Stars UK Ltd.
22 Grafton Street, London W1S 4EX
www.risingstars-uk.com

The right of Roger Hurn to be identified as the author of this work
has been asserted by him in accordance with the Copyright,
Design and Patents Act 1988.

Published 2008

Text, design and layout © Rising Stars UK Ltd.

Cover design: Burville-Riley Partnership
Illustrator: Stik, Bill Greenhead for Illustration Ltd
Text design and typesetting: Andy Wilson
Publisher: Gill Budgell
Editor: Catherine Baker

British Library Cataloguing in Publication Data.
A CIP record for this book is available from the British Library

ISBN: 978-1-84680-425-0

Printed in the UK by CPI Bookmarque, Croydon, CR0 4TD

Mixed Sources
Product group from well-managed
forests and other controlled sources
www.fsc.org Cert no. TT-COC-002227
© 1996 Forest Stewardship Council

Contents

Meet the Mystery Mob

Name:

Gummy

FYI: Gummy hasn't got much brain – and even fewer teeth.

Loves: Soup.

Hates: Toffee chews.

Fact: The brightest thing about him is his shirt.

Name:

Lee

FYI: If Lee was any cooler he'd be a cucumber.

Loves: Hip-hop.

Hates: Hopscotch.

Fact: He has his own designer label (which he peeled off a tin).

Name:

Rob

FYI: Rob lives in his own world – he's just visiting planet Earth.

Loves: Daydreaming.

Hates: Nightmares.

Fact: Rob always does his homework – he just forgets to write it down.

Name:

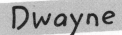
Dwayne

FYI: Dwayne is smarter than a tree full of owls.

Loves: Anything complicated.

Hates: Join-the-dots books.

Fact: If he was any brighter you could use him as a floodlight at football matches.

Name:

Chet

FYI: Chet is as brave as a lion with steel jaws.

Loves: Having adventures.

Hates: Knitting.

Fact: He's as tough as the chicken his granny cooks for his tea.

Name:

Adi

FYI: Adi is as happy as a football fan with tickets to the big match.

Loves: Telling jokes.

Hates: Moaning minnies.

Fact: He knows more jokes than a jumbo joke book.

The Joker

April Fools' Day is coming and
the Mystery Mob are worried. Every year
on 1st April, Adi always plays pranks
on them. They try not to fall for his tricks,
but he gets them every time!

Adi   I love April Fools' Day.

Chet   That's because you're such
          a joker.

Adi   You bet! Do you remember
last year? It was wicked!
I sent Gummy a piece of paper
with the words 'Please Turn Over'
written on both sides.

Chet   Yeah, it kept him busy
all morning.

Adi   And I gave Lee a boomerang
          football.

Chet   Yep, every time he kicked it,
          it kept coming back to him.
          He couldn't make a pass
          or score a goal. It drove him nuts!

Adi   Right. Then I told Dwayne
          I had a photo proving
          there really is life on Mars.
          He got so excited.

Chet   He did – until you showed him
          the photo.

Adi   It did show life on Mars!

Chet   Yeah, but it was your pet mouse
          Jumbo sitting on a Mars bar!

Adi   (giggling) And don't forget how I fooled Rob.

Chet   You told him a haggis had escaped from the zoo and there was a £50 reward for anyone who caught it.

Adi   (laughing) He spent all of April Fools' Day making a haggis trap.

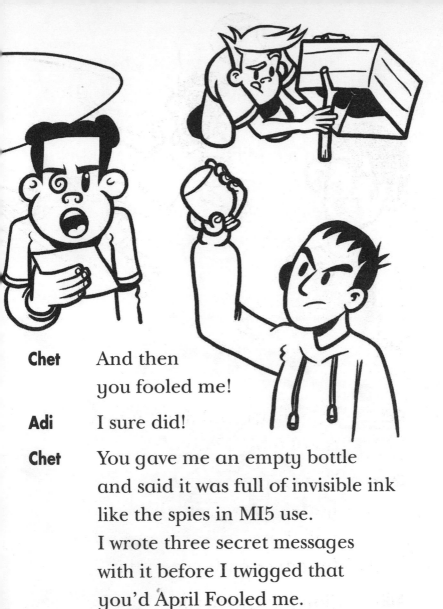

Chet   And then
you fooled me!

Adi   I sure did!

Chet   You gave me an empty bottle
and said it was full of invisible ink
like the spies in MI5 use.
I wrote three secret messages
with it before I twigged that
you'd April Fooled me.

Adi   Can I help it if you think you're
some kind of junior James Bond?

Chet   Okay, but what prank have you got planned for April Fools' Day this year?

Adi   I'm not telling you, but it'll be my best one yet. Trust me, you guys are going to be toast!

The Dark Digger

Adi is sitting at home when Chet arrives
with a DVD.

Chet   Hey, Adi. I've got this wicked DVD.
It's called *The Legend of the
Dark Digger*. Let's watch it.

Adi   What's it about?

Chet   Well, the Dark Digger is
a really scary goblin.

Adi   I don't like the sound of him.
What does he do?

Chet   He steals gold. Then he sneaks
off into the woods at night
and buries it in the ground.
That's why he's called the
Dark Digger.

Adi   Okay. Shall we call up the rest
            of the Mystery Mob and get them
            over here to watch the DVD
            with us?

Chet   No, they're all busy tonight.

Adi   That's too bad. This DVD
            sounds good.

The two boys watch the DVD.
When it's over, Chet turns to Adi.

Chet Well, what did you think of the Dark Digger DVD?

Adi It's awesome! But is the Dark Digger for real?

Chet I think so. It says on the cover that the DVD's based on a true story.

Adi Wow!

Chet Yeah. It's a shame he escapes at the end of the movie, though.

Adi That's 'cos the hero is a total wally. There's no way the Dark Digger would ever escape from me.

Chet How come?

Adi Because I'm way smarter
than any goblin.

Chet That's good, 'cos I saw this story
in the local paper. It says that
a mysterious thief is stealing gold
from all the posh houses
near here.

Adi Hey, that's what the
Dark Digger does.

Chet Yep. And get this, Adi, the cops
are looking for a small man
who dresses like a goblin!

Adi   You're kidding me.

Chet   I'm not. Look, I've got a copy of
the newspaper with me. You can
read all about it for yourself.

Chet gives Adi the paper. Adi reads
the story. He gets very excited.

Adi   Wow, I think this thief is
the Dark Digger.

Chet (thoughtfully) That makes sense.

Adi (excitedly) You bet it does!
But the Dark Digger has made
a big mistake. He may have
hoodwinked the hero in the DVD,
but now he's up against me.
It'll be no contest.

Chet So what are we waiting for?
Let's go and catch that
ghastly goblin!

3

If You Go Down to the Woods Tonight

Chet and Adi go looking for
the Dark Digger in Witches Wood.

Adi   It's a bit creepy out here, Chet.
Let's give up and go back home.

Chet Why? Are you fed up with playing
hide and shriek in these woods?

Adi   Don't you mean hide and *seek*?

Chet No, 'cos if we do find where
the Dark Digger's hiding,
I bet you'll *shriek*.

Adi   Huh, I'm not scared.

Chet   That's good, because we're in the
dead centre of the wood and I can
see something sneaking along
in those shadows over there.

Adi   (shaking) Is it the Dark Digger?

Chet   Yes. It's the right size and it's
limping, so it must be him.

Adi	Why must it be him?
Chet	'Cos the Dark Digger is a hobblin' goblin.
Adi	Doh! This is no time for jokes. What do we do next?
Chet	We're going to grab him – if you're still up for it.
Adi	Don't you worry about me, I'm ghoul. Er ... I mean cool.

Chet I'd say from the way you're shaking, you're not just cool – you're freezing!

Adi All right, if you're so brave, *you* grab him!

Chet Okay, I will!

Chet tiptoes up behind the goblin and grabs hold of it by its long black cloak. The goblin gives a blood-curdling yell. It has a really ugly face and long claws.

Adi   Gotcha!

Chet   (fiercely) Don't move,
Mr Dark Digger, or you'll
be sorry.

The goblin shakes in its boots.
It seems scared of Chet.

Adi   The game's up for you,
Dark Digger. You should never
have messed with me.

Chet   You tell him, Adi.

Adi   No – I want *him* to tell *me*
where he's hidden all the gold
he's stolen.

Chet   Good thinking! Okay,
Dark Digger, take us to the spot
where the pot of gold is buried.

The goblin nods its horrible head
and beckons for the boys to follow.

4
Making a Mark

The grim goblin leads Chet and Adi out of Witches Wood and into a big field.

Adi   Hey, Chet, this field is covered in rocks.

Chet   Maybe the farmer's growing them to make stone soup.

Adi   Don't be daft. You can't make soup with stones.

Chet   Why not? You can have rock salmon and rock candy.

Adi Chet, I don't care about the rocks, but I do care about the gold. Make him tell us where it is.

Chet (gruffly) Okay, Dark Digger, where have you hidden the pot of gold?

The goblin takes them to a rock. He points to it.

Adi   (fiercely) Are you saying the gold is under this rock?

The goblin doesn't say anything, it just nods.

Chet   Well done, Adi. You've cracked it! Gimme five.

While Adi and Chet are high fiving each other the goblin runs off into the woods. Adi gives chase, but the Dark Digger vanishes into the shadows.

Chet   I can't believe it, Adi.
The Dark Digger's given you
the slip. You said that would
never happen to you.

Adi   (crossly) Never mind what I said,
the main thing is we've got
the gold.

Chet   No, we haven't. It's buried
under that rock and we haven't
got a spade to dig it up with.

Adi   No problem, we'll nip back
        to my house and get one
        from the garden shed.

Chet   Okay. I just hope we can
        remember which rock the gold
        is hidden under. All these rocks
        look the same to me.

Adi   Hmmm … good point.
        We need to mark it in some way.

Chet   Great idea, Adi. Look, I've got
a red felt tip pen in my pocket.
Why don't I use it to make a cross
on the rock?

Adi   (smugly) Excellent thinking,
Chet. I guess a little bit
of my genius is beginning
to rub off on you at last.

Chet   I guess it must be, Adi. Thanks.

Chet Plays the Joker

Adi takes a spade from his dad's shed
and the boys hurry back to the field.
Adi can't wait to find the gold,
but he gets a nasty surprise.

Adi   I don't believe it!

Chet   Why, what's up?

Adi   We'll never find the gold now,
Chet.

Chet   Why not? It's only under a rock.

Adi   But which rock?

Chet   The rock with the red cross on it.

Adi   But look, Chet. They've all got
red crosses on them. That sneaky
goblin's nipped back here
while we were fetching the spade
and he's marked every rock
in the field.

Chet   What a joker!

Adi   Grrr! I'd like to get my hands
            on him!

Chet   Well, now's your chance, Adi –
            here he comes.

The Dark Digger walks across the field
to Chet and Adi.

Adi   I don't get it. Why have you come back? Are you going to show me where the gold is?

The Dark Digger shakes its head.

Chet   Maybe the Dark Digger wants to show you something else, Adi.

The goblin puts its claws to its face
and pulls. To Adi's horror the goblin's
face comes off it its hands.

Adi   Arrrrrgh! That's horrible.

Chet   No, it isn't – it's Rob.
           He's the Dark Digger.

Adi   What?!!

Chet   Come on out, guys.

The rest of the Mystery Mob walk out from the wood. They are all laughing.

Adi   What's going on? You said the boys were busy tonight.

Chet   That's right, Adi. We've been busy setting you up for April Fools' Day.

Adi   So the Dark Digger isn't real.

Chet   Nope.

Adi   Doh!

Chet   And now we've all got something to say to you, Adi, that we've never been able to say before.

Adi   What's that?

Mystery Mob

We've April Fooled you, Adi!

They certainly have and so,
just for once, the joke is on Adi,
the April Fools' Day joker!

About
the author

Roger Hurn has:

- had a hit record in Turkey
- won *The Weakest Link* on TV
- swum with sharks on the Great Barrier Reef.

Now he's a writer, and he hopes you like reading about the Mystery Mob as much as he likes writing about them.

April Fools' Day quiz

Questions

1 What kind of cars do lazy dogs chase?

2 What do sea monsters eat?

3 What month has 28 days?

4 Why was the baby ant confused?

5 Why did the banana go to the doctor?

6 What gets wetter the more it dries?

7 What kind of cheese is made backwards?

8 Why won't bicycles stand up
   by themselves?

Answers

1 Parked ones!
2 Fish and ships!
3 All of them!
4 All its uncles were ants!
5 Because it wasn't peeling well!
6 A towel!
7 Edam!
8 Because they're too tired! (Two-tyred – geddit?)

How did you score?

🖐 If you got all eight April Fools' Day answers correct, then you are definitely too cool to be an April Fool!

🖐 If you got six April Fools' Day answers correct, then you are nobody's fool.

🖐 If you got fewer than four April Fools' Day answers correct, then you need to stop fooling around.

When I was a kid

Question Did you ever play April Fools' Day pranks when you were a kid?

Roger Well, one April Fools' Day, I put a bald wig on my little sister and got my dad's electric razor from the bathroom. Then we went downstairs into the kitchen where our mum and dad were having their tea.

Question Did they think your prank was funny?

Roger No, Mum was so shocked that she dropped her cup of tea.

Question What did your dad do?

Roger Dad sprayed cake all down his shirt.

Question Why? Was he shocked too?

Roger No – I'd put shaving foam in his cream bun!

Adi's favourite April Fools' Day joke

What's the difference between an English April Fool and an American April Fool?

About 4000 miles!

Five fantastic facts about April Fools' Day

1 People all over the world celebrate April Fools' Day by playing jokes on each other. In England tricks can only be played in the morning.

2 In France, April Fools' Day is called Poisson d'Avril, which means April Fish. Children tape paper fish to their friends' backs and when the 'fool' finds out, the prankster yells 'Poisson d'Avril!'. Hmmm … that sounds a bit fishy to me!

3 The BBC once played an April Fools' Day joke by broadcasting the news that spaghetti grows on trees. (It doesn't, but lots of people rang the BBC asking where they could buy spaghetti trees!)

4 On 1st April 1998, Burger King advertised 'left-handed whoppers'. Lots of people came in and ordered them. I wonder if they asked for left-handed fries to go with the burgers?

5 On 1st April 1938, an American radio station broadcast a play about a Martian invasion as if it was really happening. Lots of people believed that enemy aliens from outer space had landed and ran out onto the streets in panic. Mind you, they really gave the radio station a rocket when they found out they'd been fooled!

How not to be an April Fool

When you go to bed on 31st March put a big sign at the end of your bed saying: IT'S APRIL FOOLS' DAY. That way, you'll be on your guard for pranksters from the moment you open your eyes in the morning.

When you go for a wash, check that no one's swapped the soap for 'dirty face' soap from the joke shop.

Look out for 'whoopee' cushions every time you sit down.

Do NOT be fooled if anyone you know appears to have a bandaged finger with a nasty-looking nail sticking right through it. This April Fools' Day trick is so old it's even older than me!

Make sure any prank you play on 1st April is funny both for you and the person you fool. An April Fools' joke must never be unkind or hurtful. The golden rule is: never be cruel to an April Fool.

April Fools' Day lingo

A long wait Watch out if someone sends you to the shop on 1st April and tells you to ask for 'a long wait'. You'll get one all right, but it'll take ages!

April gowk A Scottish expression for an April Fool. A gowk is a cuckoo.

Noodle What you call someone who falls for an April Fools' Day prank.

Poisson d'Avril Fish of April. This is what the French call April Fools' Day!

Prank This is a practical joke. For example, sending someone off to get you a tin of tartan paint so you can finish your picture of a Scotsman in a kilt.

Sky hooks Sky hooks don't exist. But lots of people are sent to the shops to try to buy them on April Fools' Day.

Mystery Mob

Mystery Mob Set 1:

Mystery Mob and the Abominable Snowman
Mystery Mob and the Big Match
Mystery Mob and the Circus of Doom
Mystery Mob and the Creepy Castle
Mystery Mob and the Haunted Attic
Mystery Mob and the Hidden Treasure
Mystery Mob and the Magic Bottle
Mystery Mob and the Missing Millions
Mystery Mob and the Monster on the Moor
Mystery Mob and the Mummy's Curse
Mystery Mob and the Time Machine
Mystery Mob and the UFO

Mystery Mob Set 2:

Mystery Mob and the Ghost Town
Mystery Mob and the Bonfire Night Plot
Mystery Mob and the April Fools' Day Joker
Mystery Mob and the Great Pancake Day Race
Mystery Mob and the Scary Santa
Mystery Mob and the Conker Conspiracy
Mystery Mob and the Top Talent Contest
Mystery Mob and the Night in the Waxworks
Mystery Mob and the Runaway Train
Mystery Mob and the Wrong Robot
Mystery Mob and the Day of the Dinosaurs
Mystery Mob and the Man-eating Tiger

RISING★STARS